MW00395316

Halloween Celebration
Lisa Bastien & Lori Bastien

Halloween is a time for dress up, make believe, decorating, pumpkin carving, and many other fun festivities! Join in the excitement of Halloween with this holiday collection, perfect for beginning students in the early to late elementary levels. **Halloween Celebration** provides a variety of motivating pieces that will captivate your students' imagination and interest.

Contents

ISBN 0-8497-9621-0

Old MacDonald's Ghost

Lisa Bastien

Moderato

Lyrics:
Old Mac-Don-ald had a ghost who lived be-hind a post. On Hal-lo-ween he came to play. He scared the kids a-way. With a boo, boo, here and a boo, boo, there. Here a boo, there a boo, ev-'ry-where a boo, boo. Sun came up the ghost ran fast for Hal-lo-ween had passed!

WP400

COSTUME PARTY

Lori Bastien

Steady rock beat

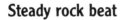

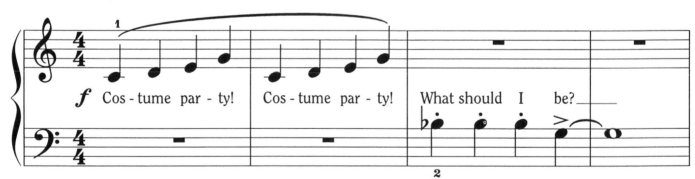

Cos - tume par - ty! Cos - tume par - ty! What should I be?

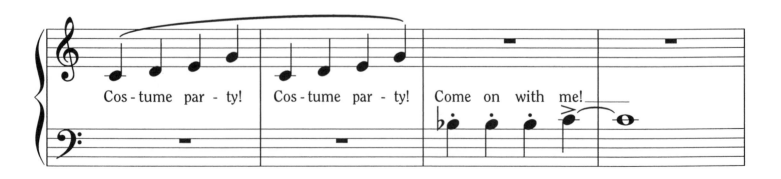

Cos - tume par - ty! Cos - tume par - ty! Come on with me!

Come to my house, won't you? Come to my cos - tume par - ty.

Let's get this ball roll - ing! It's Hal - lo - ween.

Cos - tume par - ty! Cos - tume par - ty! Don't you be late!

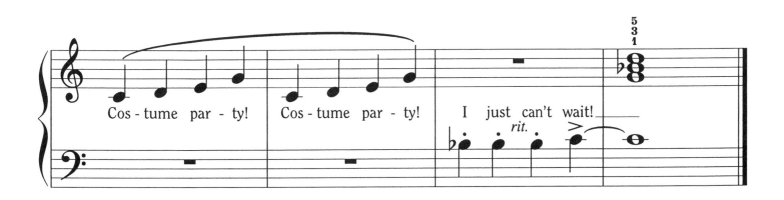

Cos - tume par - ty! Cos - tume par - ty! I just can't wait!

rit.

Alone on Halloween

Lori Bastien

Adagio

mf Here I am in - side by the door, cold and lone - ly and on the floor.

E - ven though to - night's Hal - lo - ween, this great pump - kin won't be seen.

The Halloween Star

Lisa Bastien

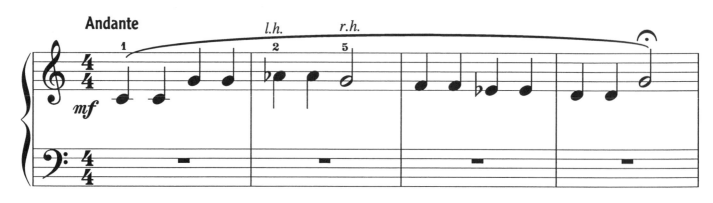

I'm a lit-tle star who lives up in the sky. I light the night as the kids go by.

Halloween Carnival

Lori Bastien

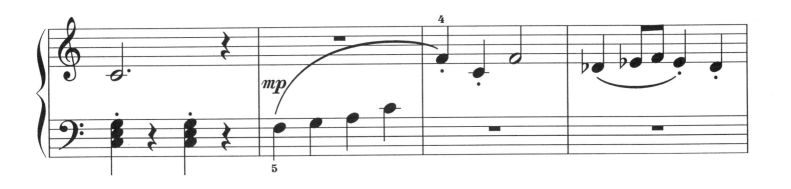

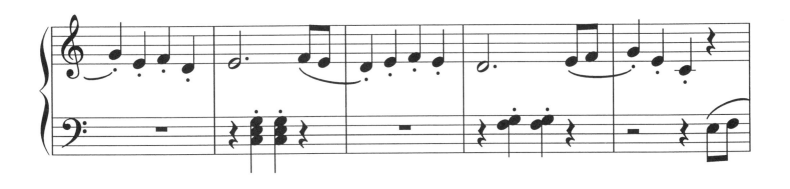

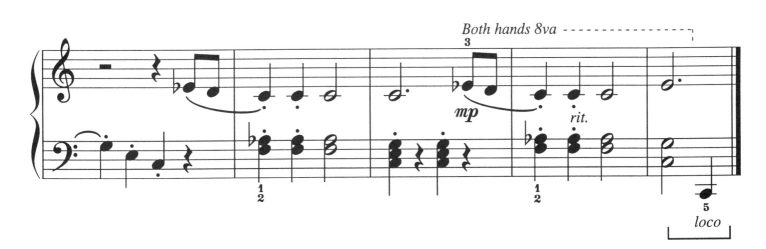

noises in the night
(Chopin's Halloween)

Arranged by Lisa Bastien

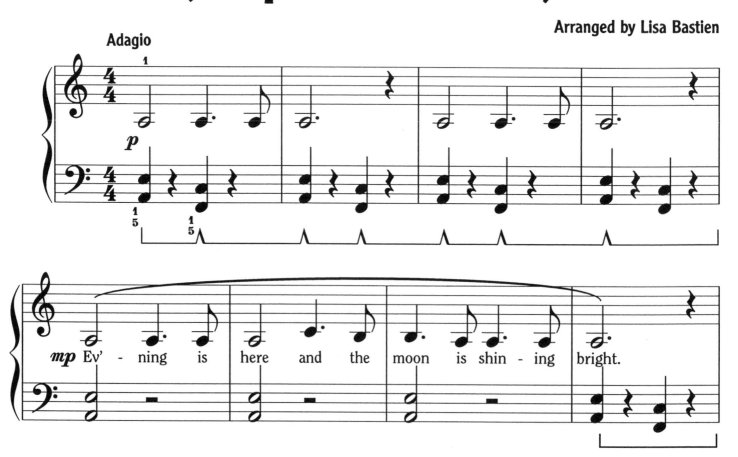

Ev' - ning is here and the moon is shin - ing bright.

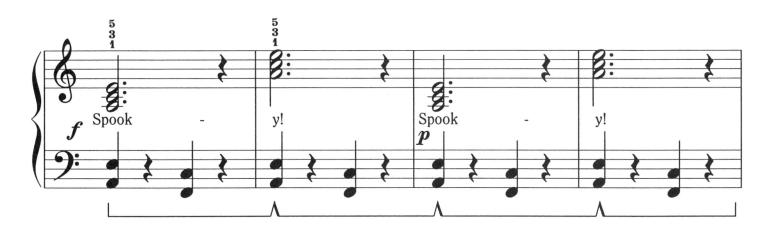

OLD HAUNTED HOUSE

Lori Bastien

Slowly

mp

Watch out for that | old haunt-ed house! | Watch out! It's as | qui-et as a mouse.

mf

If you en-ter | all the way in-side, | hope you're read-y | for a spook-y ride.

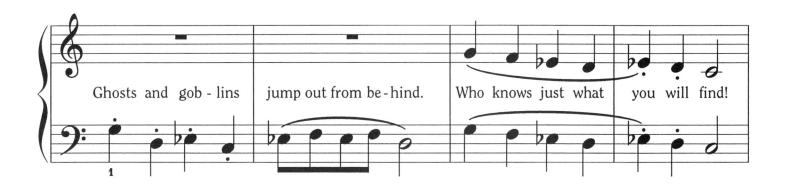

Ghosts and gob-lins jump out from be-hind. Who knows just what you will find!

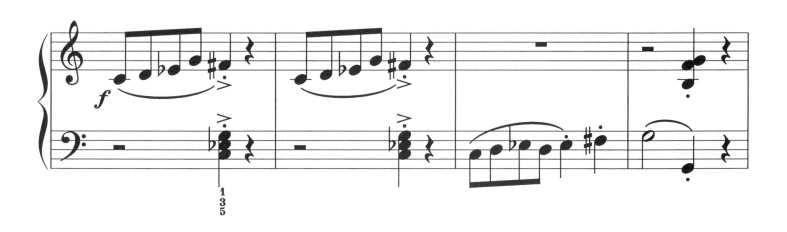

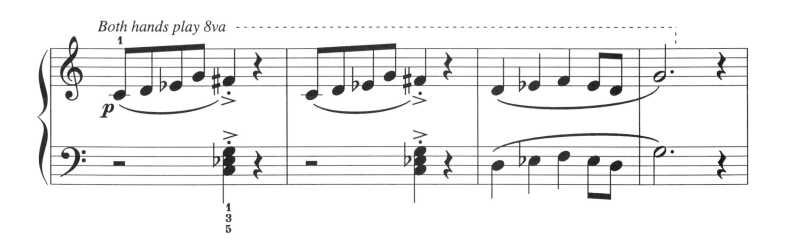

Both hands play 8va

Watch out for that old haunt-ed house. Watch out! It's as qui-et as a mouse!

BLACK CAT BALLAD

Lori Bastien

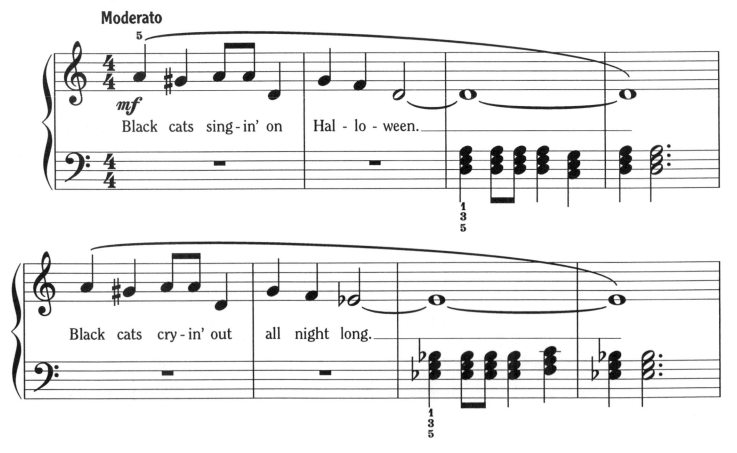

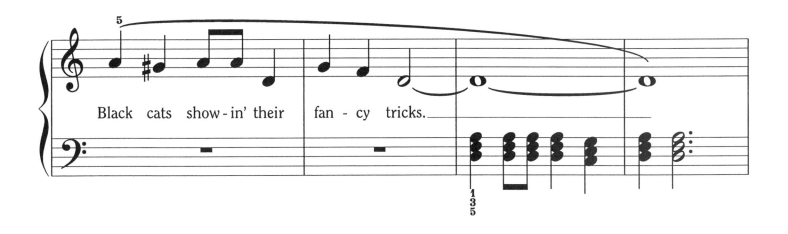

Black cats show-in' their fan-cy tricks.

Fine

Hal - lo - ween, Hal - lo - ween night.

rit. 2nd time

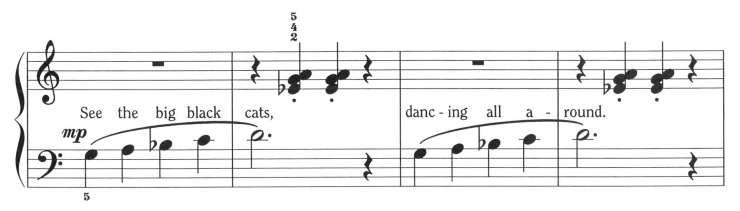

See the big black cats, danc-ing all a - round.

mp

D.C. al Fine

Lis - ten to their screams! They sure love Hal - lo - ween.

rit.

WP400

Monster Rock

Lisa Bastien

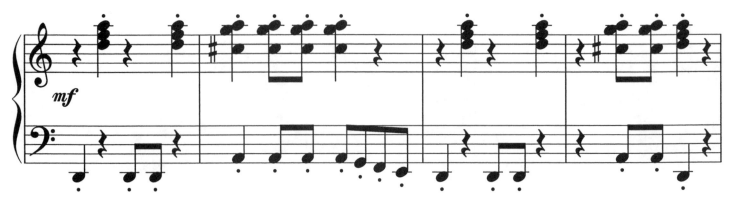

Jack-o-lantern's Grin

Lori Bastien

bright! Some look spook-y, some look kind of wild, some seem ver-y sad.

Some look fun-ny, some are oh, so glad. Some look ver-y, ver-y mad!

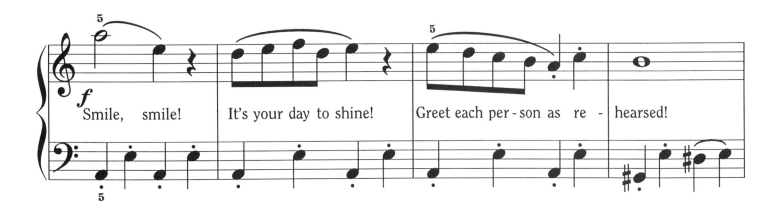

Smile, smile! It's your day to shine! Greet each per-son as re - hearsed!

Jack-O'-lan-tern's grin, Jack-O'-lan-tern's grin, on Oc-tob-er thir-ty first!

8va

On the Prowl

Lisa Bastien

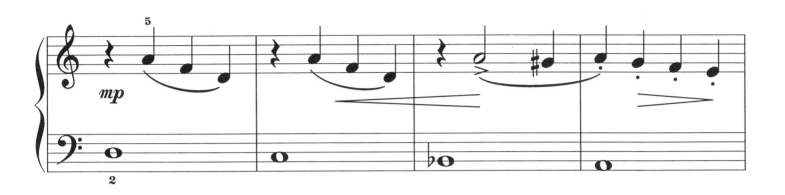

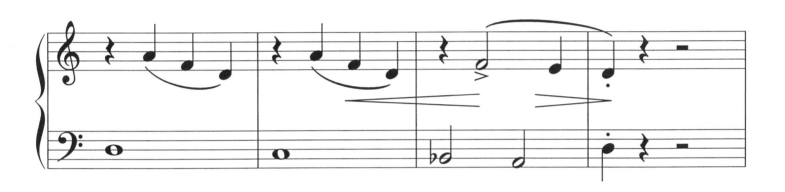

About the Composers

Lisa Bastien began piano lessons at the young age of four, studying with her mother at the Preparatory Department of Tulane University. She received her Bachelor of Music in Piano Performance from Drake University and her Master's degree in piano pedagogy from Arizona State University. After completing her master's degree, Lisa moved to New Orleans and taught in the Preparatory Department of Loyola University. Lisa Bastien, her husband Basil Hanss, and their two daughters now reside in New York City, where Lisa continues to teach private and group lessons and compose fun and motivational music for her students. To encourage learning and reinforce musical concepts, Lisa developed ideas for the handy **Wipe-Off** and **Dot-to-Dot** books and, with her sister Lori, coauthored the **Theory Booster Series** activity books, focusing on elements of music theory. Lisa is also a coauthor of the **Bastien Adult Piano Course**.

Lori Bastien began lessons at age four, also studying with her mother. After attending the University of Redlands, Lori transferred to Rice University where she received her Bachelor of Music degree. She teaches both group and private lessons and is very active in local and national music teacher organizations. Teaching piano since her teen years, Lori writes music that her students find fun to play. She coauthored **Bastien's Invitation to Music** and **A Debut for You** (Books 1-4) and **Bastien Adult Piano Course** with her mother Jane and her sister Lisa. Also with her sister, she coauthored the **Theory Booster Series** activity books. Lori, her husband Eric Vickers, and their two children live in La Jolla, California.